My Best Friend

Written and Illustrated by   Joy V. Dueland

The Christian Science Publishing Society
Boston, Massachusetts, U. S. A.

What is a friend?
Someone who gives you the biggest half of a cookie.

Someone who likes you more than a little.
Someone who walks the long way
        home with you.

Someone who
    gets you out of trouble—
        and doesn't tell.

A friend's someone who likes a lot to be with you
and doesn't care that you're smaller.

Someone who sticks up for you when you need him.

That's what a friend is.

But what's a *best* friend?
A friend who's more.

A friend who likes you more
than anybody's liked you—ever.

A friend who'd do more for you
than anybody ever would.

I've got a best friend.
My best friend is God.

God never leaves me,
even when I sleep.

When I'm not happy,
 I remember how He loves me.
Then I can smile again.

I can't see God — but I can see His work all around me.

God's love is the reason for the rainbow.
God's love is behind the gentle things
and all the good that happens.

God's love heals every hurt,
no matter how bad.

His love gives me all that I need,
and leaves no one out.

My father and mother are His children, too.
He is our heavenly Father and Mother.

He is the best friend to all of us,
big and little.

If I'm cross and tired, then I think of God—

and I'm not cross or tired anymore.

God gives me more than any friend has ever given me.

God gives me His love to love with

so I can be a best friend

— to everyone.

Note to Parents

Throughout the centuries, friendship has been associated with God. In the Old Testament we hear of Jonathan saying to his great friend David, "The Lord be between me and thee." [1] And Jesus said to his beloved disciples, "As the Father hath loved me, so have I loved you . . . I have called you friends; for all things that I have heard of my Father I have made known unto you." [2]

Friendship, in this highest sense, has deep implications. Mary Baker Eddy says, "Pure humanity, friendship, home, the interchange of love, bring to earth a foretaste of heaven." [3]

To awaken in a child this sense of heaven on earth, and to foster an abiding trust in God who is his and everyone's best friend, this book has been written.

[1] I Sam. 20:42; [2] John 15:9, 15; [3] *Miscellaneous Writings* (p. 100) by Mary Baker Eddy, the Discoverer and Founder of Christian Science and author of its textbook, *Science and Health with Key to the Scriptures.*